This publication by the **Bible Society** © BFBS 1980
146 Queen Victoria Street, London EC4V 4BX
Text from the Good News Bible
published by the Bible Societies/Collins
© American Bible Society, New York 1966, 1971, 1976

BFBS 1980 15M TEV670/104 ISBN 0 564 04002 9

INTRODUCTION

First Steps in Faith has been written to help people who have just started the Christian life to find out more about how to live as Christians.

It is the second in the Steps in Faith series and it builds on First Steps to Faith. There are ten sessions, focusing on Faith, Freedom and Love. They deal with how we are put right with God and what it means to have faith. From there, those doing the sessions will proceed step by step to consider why God sent Jesus, how Jesus should change the way we live and how we can show Jesus to others.

So, the aim of First Steps in Faith is to help people learn how to live as God wants them to live.

FIRST STEPS IN FAITH

HOW TO USE THIS BOOK

Things to know before you start

1. First Steps in Faith is mainly for use with groups, but it can be used by individuals. Whichever way you use it, all you need with the book is a pencil or pen and you will be ready to go.

2. It is meant to follow on from First Steps to Faith. So, make sure that the people using the booklet look through the work they did in First Steps to Faith before beginning this set of sessions. If you did not use First Steps to Faith, here are some important things that you should know before starting this booklet.

   First Steps to Faith considered:

   * How the world began and what it's like today
   * Why things went wrong in the world
   * What God thinks of the way man behaves
   * Jesus —
     who he was;
     what he did;
     what he said;
     why he died;
     how people in the Bible reacted to him;
     how each individual doing First Steps to Faith reacts to him.

   If you have not thought through these issues you should spend some time doing so before proceeding.

3. All the Bible passages are taken from the Good News Bible.

4. The aim for each session is presented under the session title e.g. Session One, Faith: Finding out about being friends with God.

5. An action point means that each individual decides to take one thing that they have particularly learnt and act upon it before the next session, e.g. My action point for this week is: To try harder to live as Jesus wants me to by thinking about other people's feelings more.

How to use First Steps in Faith with Groups

1. Ideally, there should be no more than ten people in the group.

2. If possible the chairs in the room should be arranged in a circle, so that everybody can see each other.

3. This booklet will take eleven sessions to work through because the group will need to meet together once before starting Session One.

4. The group should allow two hours for each session.

At the group's first meeting
1. Have some tea or coffee ready to give to people as they arrive.

2. It is important that the group should get to know each other before starting the sessions. If they have not worked together as a group before, here are two exercises you could use to help them to find out about each other:

Either
a) Make sure that each member has a pen and a piece of paper.
b) Ask them to write four things on it.
i) Their Christian name (in the centre of the page).
ii) Two people that mean a lot to them (top right-hand corner).
iii) Their favourite TV programme (top left-hand corner).
iv) The most important thing(s) that they think the group should know about them (bottom of the page).
Allow 5-10 minutes for each person to do this.

The page should look like this:

Favourite TV Show	Two important people
Name	
Important thing(s) the group should know about me	

c) Go around the group asking people to say what they have written and to explain why. (Do not ask each person to talk about all four statements in one go.) Get each person to start with their name. Having gone round the group move on to their favourite TV programme and so on. Try not to work straight round the group. Change the order in which you ask each person for their answers each time.

or

a) Split the group into pairs.

b) Ask them to find out as much as they can about their partner in

3

five minutes. Tell them to be prepared to report back to the whole group on what their partner has said.
Allow 10 minutes for chatting.

c) Bring the group back together.

d) Move round the group asking people to share what they have learnt.

3. The group should then decide how to run the sessions. You can either have one person to lead all the sessions or have a different member of the group lead it in turn.

4. It is also important to decide whether the group members are going to work through the session before they arrive or do it all at the meeting. It is best if they do the work at home first.

At the Sessions

1. When all the group members have arrived, the person leading them should allow about five minutes for the group to get used to each other again. Possibly even allow time for a cup of tea or coffee before beginning. The leader should then give a brief summary of previous sessions so that they are fresh in everybody's mind.

2. Ask each member of the group to share how they have got on with their action point for the last week.

3. Read the aim of the session and make sure that everyone understands it clearly.

4. If the session has already been prepared, then get each member of the group to share their answers.

5. If you are planning to do all the work at the meeting, allow about ten minutes for the group to complete each question series. Then get them to share their answers with each other.

6. Work your way through the sessions. The leaders should make sure that each set of questions is clearly linked with the next passage and set of questions.

7. At the end of the session, the leader should draw out the issues that have been raised, encourage the group to discuss them and reach a conclusion as a result of the sessions.

8. Ask each member to tell the group their action point for the next week.

9. Remind the group that before coming to the next session it is helpful if they have at least read through the material. If it applies to your group, remind them to go through the session and answer the questions before they arrive.

10. Close the evening with tea or coffee and a chat.

How to use First Steps in Faith by yourself

1. Find a convenient time (probably about an hour), either once a day or once a week, and do a First Steps in Faith session regularly.

2. Think about how you got on with your action point since the last session.

3. Think about the aim of each session and keep it in mind throughout the session.

4. Read through the previous sessions so that they are fresh in your mind.

5. Work through the session carefully, answering all the questions as you go along.

6. Having come to the end of each session, think through all you have read and how you have answered the questions. Link this with all the other sessions.

7. Consider what conclusions you can draw from the session.

8. Decide upon your next action point.

9. Make sure that you do the next session without too much delay so that you are still thinking about what you have learned in the meantime.

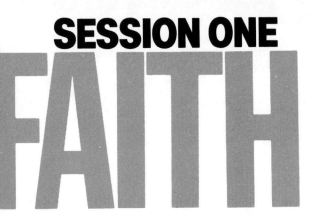

Finding out about being right with God.

At the end of the last session of First Steps to Faith we asked, "What does being right with God mean to you?" In this book we ask, "How should we live now that we are right with God?" Jesus said:

"The teachers of the Law and the Pharisees are the authorized interpreters of Moses' Law. So you must obey and follow everything they tell you to do; do not, however, imitate their actions, because they don't practise what they preach. They tie on to people's backs loads that are heavy and hard to carry, yet they aren't willing even to lift a finger to help them carry those loads. They do everything so that people will see them. Look at the straps with scripture verses on them which they wear on their foreheads and arms, and notice how large they are! Notice also how long are the tassels on their cloaks! They love the best places at feasts and the reserved seats in the synagogues; they love to be greeted with respect in the market-places and to be called 'Teacher'. You must not be called 'Teacher', because you are all brothers of one another and have only one Teacher. And you must not call anyone here on earth 'Father', because you have only the one Father in heaven. Nor should you be called 'Leader', because your one and only leader is the Messiah. The greatest one among you must be your servant. Whoever makes himself great will be humbled, and whoever humbles himself will be made great."

Matthew 23.2-12

The Pharisees were:
* a religious party in the time of Jesus
* careful to keep the laws of Moses and other Jewish regulations wherever they were because they thought that it was only if they did this that God would put them right with himself
* liberal-minded Jews who believed in life after death
* mostly gentlemen who wanted the law to be a joy not a burden

In this passage Jesus talks about people not practising what they preach. What do you think Jesus means when he talks about this?

I think Jesus means:

_____

_____

_____

The passage also talks about putting loads on other people's backs. What do you think Jesus means?

I think Jesus means:

_____

_____

_____

Having read this passage, I think Jesus thought that the law was: (Tick one)

a) Not to be taken seriously.
b) Very important.
c) To be taken seriously but not to be seen as a burden.
d)
_____

Read what Paul said:

Now that we have been put right with God through faith, we have peace with God through our Lord Jesus Christ. He has brought us by faith into this experience of God's grace, in which we now live. And so we boast of the hope we have of sharing God's glory! We also boast of our troubles, because we know that trouble produces endurance, endurance brings God's approval, and his approval creates hope. This hope does not disappoint us, for God has poured out his love into our hearts by means of the Holy Spirit, who is God's gift to us.

For when we were still helpless, Christ died for the wicked at the time that God chose. It is a difficult thing for someone to die for a righteous person. It may even be that someone might dare to die for a good person. But God has shown us how much he loves us — it was while we were still sinners that Christ died for us! By his death we are now put right with God; how much more, then, will we be saved by him from God's anger! We were God's enemies, but he made us his friends through the death of his Son. Now that we are God's friends, how much more will we be saved by Christ's life! But that is not all; we rejoice because of what God has done through our Lord Jesus Christ, who has now made us God's friends.

Romans 5.1-11

Paul was a Pharisee and he had tried to stop people believing in Jesus. He came to see who Jesus really was and began to tell others. (Read about it in Acts 9.)

These passages talk about two different ways of being right with God. What do you think this means?

I think that to be right with God you need to: (Tick one)

a) Work very hard to come up to God's standard.
b) Make sure that you act like Jesus did.
c) Have faith in Jesus Christ and his death for you.
d) Be as good as you can.
e) _____

The passages also say that we can be friends with God through Jesus Christ. Write down what it means to you to be right with God.

Paul wrote about some of the gifts God's people have because they are right with God.

He said that:
a) They had been put right with God through _____

8

b) They had been brought into an experience of God's _____

c) Because of God's approval they could now have _____

These gifts are really important — learn why in the next sessions.

My action point for this week is:

_____

_____

_____

SESSION TWO

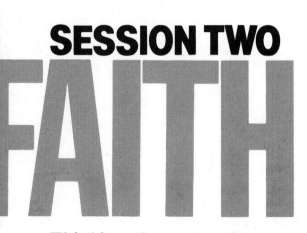

Thinking about what it means to have faith.

This is how I got on with my action point. I found that

_____

_____

_____

Last session we wanted to make the point that:

God makes us right with him; <u>we</u> can't do it. To be right with God you need faith.

Read about the Canaanite woman:

Jesus left that place and went off to the territory near the cities of Tyre and Sidon. A Canaanite woman who lived in that region came to him. "Son of David!" she cried out.

"Have mercy on me! My daughter has a demon and is in a terrible condition."

But Jesus did not say a word to her. His disciples came to

him and begged him, "Send her away! She is following us and making all this noise!"

Then Jesus replied, "I have been sent only to those lost sheep, the people of Israel."

At this the woman came and fell at his feet. "Help me, sir!" she said.

Jesus answered, "It isn't right to take the children's food and throw it to the dogs."

"That's true, sir," she answered; "but even the dogs eat the leftovers that fall from their masters' table."

So Jesus answered her, "You are a woman of great faith! What you want will be done for you." And at that very moment her daughter was healed.

Matthew 15.21-28

1. Why do you think Jesus did not send her away?

I think Jesus didn't send her away because: (Tick one)
a) She was not worth the effort.
b) He wanted to test whether she had faith.
c) He wanted to be kind to her.
d) He knew she had faith and wanted to let her show it.
e) _____

2. How do you think the Canaanite woman felt when her daughter was healed?

Make a list of words that describe how she felt.

3. There are lots of important things to learn about faith in this story. What is the most important to you?

For me, the most important thing about faith in this story is:

_____

_____

_____

_____

In First Steps to Faith, Session 4 dealt with God's law and man's behaviour. We also thought about how we decide what's right and what's wrong.

Now read what Paul said:

But now God's way of putting people right with himself has been revealed. It has nothing to do with law, even though the Law of Moses and the prophets gave their witness to it. God puts people right through their faith in Jesus Christ. God does this to all who believe in Christ, because there is no difference at all: everyone has sinned and is far away from God's saving presence. But by the free gift of God's grace all are put right with him through Christ Jesus, who sets them free. God offered him, so that by his death he should become the means by which people's sins are forgiven through their faith in him. God did this in order to demonstrate that he is righteous. In the past he was patient and overlooked people's sins; but in the present time he deals with their sins, in order to demonstrate his righteousness. In this way God shows that he himself is righteous and that he puts right everyone who believes in Jesus.

What then, can we boast about? Nothing! And what is the reason for this? Is it that we obey the Law? No, but that we believe. For we conclude that a person is put right with God only through faith, and not by doing what the Law commands. Or is God the God of the Jews only? Is he not the God of the Gentiles also? Of course he is. God is one, and he will put the Jews right with himself on the basis of their faith, and will put the Gentiles right through their faith. Does this mean that by this faith we do away with the Law? No, not at all; instead, we uphold the Law.

Romans 3.21-31

This passage contrasts law and faith. Let's see how. Mark the references to faith in the passage in one way and those to the law in another. (You could use two different colour pens.) Don't be surprised if you get two marks under some words.

Now let's think about law.

Which of these statements describe what you think of when you hear the word law:

Put them in order by putting numbers beside each balloon.
(1 = the one you think of most often)
(5 = the one you think of least often)

God did more than make rules for us. He dealt with our sin. What does this mean to you?

For Jesus to deal with my sins means

_____

_____

_____

Paul says Jesus sets us free.
To me, being set free through Jesus means: (Tick one)
a) That I can keep the commandments.
b) That my sins are forgiven.
c) That I don't have to keep the commandments.
d) _____

God's law isn't just rules. It's a sign of God's love.

God begins the Ten Commandments by saying:

"I am the LORD your God, who rescued you from Egypt, where you were slaves."   **Deuteronomy 5.6**

He said this to show that he loved his people before they had his law to keep.

> * We don't really get the point about God's law unless we really know that God loves us.
> * God shows his love through Jesus.
> * We recognize this by faith.

Next session we'll think about the link between Jesus and the law.

My action point for this week is:

_____

_____

_____

SESSION THREE

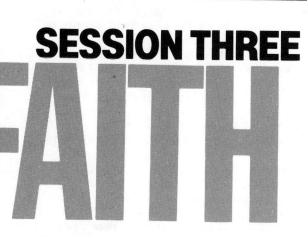

Considering God's law and his promise of Jesus.

This is how I got on with my action point. I found

_____

_____

_____

Last session we should all have learnt something about what it means to have faith in Jesus Christ. I learnt that to have faith in Jesus Christ means:

_____

_____

_____

Paul wrote about the link between God's law and Jesus. He said:

My brothers, I am going to use an everyday example: when two people agree on a matter and sign an agreement, no one can break it or add anything to it. Now, God made his promises to Abraham and to his

descendant. The scripture does not use the plural "descendants," meaning many people, but the singular "descendant," meaning one person only, namely, Christ. What I mean is that God made a covenant with Abraham and promised to keep it. The Law, which was given four hundred and thirty years later, cannot break that covenant and cancel God's promise. For if God's gift depends on the Law, then it no longer depends on his promise. However, it was because of his promise that God gave that gift to Abraham.

What, then, was the purpose of the Law? It was added in order to show what wrongdoing is, and it was meant to last until the coming of Abraham's descendant, to whom the promise was made. The Law was handed down by angels, with a man acting as a go-between. But a go-between is not needed when only one person is involved; and God is one.

Does this mean that the Law is against God's promises? No, not at all! For if mankind had received a law that could bring life, then everyone could be put right with God by obeying it. But the scripture says that the whole world is under the power of sin; and so the gift which is promised on the basis of faith in Jesus Christ is given to those who believe.

But before the time for faith came, the Law kept us all locked up as prisoners until this coming faith should be revealed. And so the Law was in charge of us until Christ came, in order that we might then be put right with God through faith. Now that the time for faith is here, the Law is no longer in charge of us.

It is through faith that all of you are God's sons in union with Christ Jesus. You were baptized into union with Christ, and now you are clothed, so to speak, with the life of Christ himself. So there is no difference between Jews and Gentiles, between slaves and free men, between men and women; you are all one in union with Christ Jesus. If you belong to Christ, then you are the descendants of Abraham and will receive what God has promised.

Galatians 3.15-29

Why do you think God gave the law?

I think God gave the law: (Tick one)
a) To keep us in our place.
b) So that he could punish us.
c) Because he loved us and was concerned about how we lived.
d) To make us good enough for him to love us.
e) _____

When you bring up children you give them rules to obey:
"Don't play with the electric fire!"
"You must be in by 9pm!"

Which of these statements expresses your attitude to these rules?
a) If you keep the rules I will love you.
b) I love you already, that's why I want you to keep the rules.

God's answer for us is b). He gave us the law because he loved
us. But rules could not make us right with him.

In the Bible, Salvation started off as:
* Israel expecting God to set them free from their enemies.
* Eventually the people of Israel realized that this physical rescue
  was impossible.
* So they looked for rescue outside of history.
* This rescue would be brought about by God's special agent, the
  Messiah.
* The early Christians believed that Jesus was the expected
  Messiah.
  (Jesus's name in Hebrew is Joshua, which means Salvation.)

Now read about baby Jesus:

At that time there was a man named Simeon living in Jerusalem. He was a good, devout man and was waiting for Israel to be saved. The Holy Spirit was with him and had assured him that he would not die before he had seen the Lord's promised Messiah. Led by the Spirit, Simeon went into the Temple. When the parents brought the child Jesus into the Temple to do for him what the Law required, Simeon took the child in his arms and gave thanks to God:
"Now, Lord, you have kept your promise,
and you may let your servant go in peace.
With my own eyes I have seen your salvation,
which you have prepared in the presence of all peoples:
A light to reveal your will to the Gentiles
and bring glory to your people Israel."

The child's father and mother were amazed at the things Simeon said about him. Simeon blessed them and said to Mary, his mother, "This child is chosen by God for the destruction and the salvation of many in Israel. He will be a sign from God which many people will speak against and so reveal their secret thoughts. And sorrow, like a sharp sword, will break your own heart."

Luke 2.25-35

What do you think Simeon meant when he spoke about Jesus?

I think Simeon meant that

_____

_____

_____

How do you think Mary and Joseph felt when they heard what Simeon said?

I think Mary and Joseph must have felt: (Tick one)
a) Very surprised by what Simeon said.
b) That they knew Jesus was very special.
c) That Simeon was mad.
d) Very confused.
e) _____

Having read this story, what do you feel about Jesus?

I feel

_____

_____

_____

> ★ Jesus is God's new way of showing that he loves us and cares about how we live.
> ★ Simeon is saying that Jesus fulfils God's promise of rescue.

Jesus said:

"Do not think that I have come to do away with the Law of Moses and the teachings of the prophets. I have not come to do away with them, but to make their teachings come true." Matthew 5.17

In First Steps to Faith Session 4 we read Jesus's summary of the commandments. (You can find this in Mark 12.28-31.) Jesus gives us the power to live by them.

My action point for this week is:

_____

_____

_____

Finding out about Jesus's power.

This is how I got on with my action point. I found that

_____

_____

_____

Jesus often spoke to people that others ignored:

Jesus went back again to the shore of Lake Galilee. A crowd came to him, and he started teaching them. As he walked along, he saw a tax collector, Levi son of Alphaeus, sitting in his office. Jesus said to him, "Follow me." Levi got up and followed him.

Later on Jesus was having a meal in Levi's house. A large number of tax collectors and other outcasts was following Jesus, and many of them joined him and his disciples at the table. Some teachers of the Law, who were Pharisees, saw that Jesus was eating with these outcasts and tax collectors, so they asked his disciples, "Why does he eat with such people?"

Jesus heard them and answered, "People who are well do not need a doctor, but only those who are sick. I have not come to call respectable people, but outcasts."

Mark 2.13-17

Tax collectors were social outcasts because:
* they worked for the Roman government
* people thought that they swindled the Jews

What do you think an outcast is?

I think an outcast is

_____

_____

Why do you think Jesus spoke to Levi, who was an outcast?

I think Jesus spoke to Levi

_____

_____

_____

Imagine how Levi must have felt when Jesus spoke to him.

When Jesus spoke to him, Levi must have felt: (Tick one)
a) Very happy.
b) Amazed.
c) That Jesus was very stupid.
d) That he would do anything for Jesus.
e) _____

* Social outcasts had no power to make people accept them — they would always be outcasts.
* Jesus cared for these people and showed his power to change the way people live.

Paul had troubles too:

But to keep me from being puffed up with pride because of the many wonderful things I saw, I was given a painful physical ailment, which acts as Satan's messenger to beat me and keep me from being proud. Three times I prayed to the Lord about this and asked him to take it away. But his answer was: "My grace is all you need, for my power is strongest when you are weak." I am most happy, then, to be proud of my weaknesses, in order to feel the protection of Christ's power over me. I am content with weaknesses, insults, hardships, persecutions, and difficulties for Christ's sake. For when I am weak, then I am strong.

2 Corinthians 12.7-10

We are all proud at times. Which of these things are you proud about? (Put a tick by all that apply)
a) I help my neighbours.
b) I keep myself to myself.
c) My car.
d) My children.
e) My house.
f) _____

Is it right to be proud about these things?

If it isn't right, think of some things that you <u>can</u> be proud about as a Christian. Write them in the box below:

Ask God to help you to be proud about the right things.

The people insulted Paul because he told them that Jesus loved them. Have you been insulted because you believe in Jesus? When?

I was insulted when

_____

_____

_____

Paul says that he feels God's power most when he feels weakest.

Have you ever felt God's protection? When was it? Write about it here:

Paul had troubles. We have troubles. Find out why next week.

My action point for this week is:

_____

_____

_____

SESSION FIVE
FAITH

Finding out how Jesus gives us hope and real happiness.

This is how I got on with my action point. I found that

_____

_____

_____

Last session we learnt about God's power in us. What did you learn?

I learnt that

_____

_____

_____

Peter talked about having difficulties too:

Let us give thanks to the God and Father of our Lord Jesus Christ! Because of his great mercy he gave us new life by raising Jesus Christ from death. This fills us with a living hope, and so we look forward to possessing the rich blessings that God keeps for his people. He keeps them for you in heaven, where they cannot decay or spoil or fade away. They are for you, who through faith are kept safe by God's power for the salvation which is ready to be revealed at the end of time.

Be glad about this, even though it may now be necessary for you to be sad for a while because of the many kinds of trials you suffer. Their purpose is to prove that your faith is genuine. Even gold, which can be destroyed, is tested by fire; and so your faith, which is much more precious than gold, must also be tested, so that it may endure. Then you will receive praise and glory and honour on the Day when Jesus Christ is revealed. You love him, although you have not seen him, and you believe in him, although you do not now see him. So you rejoice with a great and glorious joy which words cannot express, because you are receiving the salvation of your souls, which is the purpose of your faith in him.

It was concerning this salvation that the prophets made careful search and investigation, and they prophesied about this gift which God would give you. They tried to find out when the time would be and how it would come. This was the time to which Christ's Spirit in them was pointing, in predicting the sufferings that Christ would have to endure and the glory that would follow. God revealed to these prophets that their work was not for their own benefit, but for yours, as they spoke about those things which you have now heard from the messengers who announced the Good News by the power of the Holy Spirit sent from heaven. These are things which even the angels would like to understand.

1 Peter 1.3-12

We all hope for things. Which of these have you hoped for?
a) A happy marriage.
b) Lots of money.
c) A new car.
d) Promotion in my job.
e) To have good health.
f) _____

Put them in order by marking a number under each letter in the box below: (1 = most hoped for; 6 = least hoped for)

A	B	C	D	E	F

* In the Bible, hope started off as the expectation of the physical rescue of Israel.
* When the people of Israel realized this could not happen, they hoped for rescue outside of history.
* That rescue would mean that they were no longer prisoners to evil.
* This rescue that they hoped for would give them New Life.

Read about a man who hoped to be healed:

After this, Jesus went to Jerusalem for a religious festival. Near the Sheep Gate in Jerusalem there is a pool with five porches; in Hebrew it is called Bethzatha. A large crowd of sick people were lying in the porches — the blind, the lame, and the paralysed. A man was there who had been ill for thirty-eight years. Jesus saw him lying there, and he knew that the man had been ill for such a long time; so he asked him, "Do you want to get well?"

The sick man answered, "Sir, I have no one here to put me in the pool when the water is stirred up; while I am trying to get in, somebody else gets there first."

Jesus said to him, "Get up, pick up your mat, and walk." Immediately the man got well; he picked up his mat and started walking.

John 5.1-9a

How do you think he felt when Jesus came along and healed him? Draw a picture, or write a few sentences about how he felt.

What does this story tell us about Jesus's ability to fulfil hope?

It says to me that

_____

_____

_____

> The man waited at the pool because he believed he could be healed. He didn't know that it would be Jesus that healed him. Christians know that they can put their faith in Jesus Christ.

Mark the statement which most exactly expresses why you think God allows us to face trials.

I think God allows us to face trials:
a) So that we don't have things too easy.
b) Because he can't stop them.
c) To make sure that our faith in Jesus Christ is real.
d) To make us stronger.
e) _____

The word "blessing" means real happiness.
Jesus talks about real happiness in Matthew 5.3-12.

God has real happiness in store for us. When you think of happiness, what does it mean to you?

When I think of being happy, I think of

_____

_____

_____

God made the man at the pool happy through Jesus. He can make us happy too. His gifts for us will be far beyond anything we can imagine.

Peter says we should give thanks to God. Sometimes this is hard to do. When do you find it hard to do?

I find it hard to thank God when: (Tick as many as apply)
a) Everything seems to be going wrong.
b) Things go well, but I think it's all because of me.
c) The kids scream all day.
d) I've burnt the dinner.
e) I've smashed up the car.
f) _____

Look back to session 4. What did Paul say happened when he felt weak?

Paul said that when he felt weak

_____

_____

_____

Now write out the first two sentences of 1 Peter 1.3

_____

_____

_____

Try to remember this next time things go wrong.

My action point for this week is:

_____

_____

_____

SESSION SIX
FREEDOM

Finding out about how Jesus sets us free.

This is how I got on with my action point. I found

_____

_____

_____

The first time Jesus spoke about why he had come, he said that
his main purpose was to set people free:

Then Jesus went to Nazareth,
where he had been brought
up, and on the Sabbath he
went as usual to the
synagogue. He stood up to
read the Scriptures and was
handed the book of the
prophet Isaiah. He unrolled
the scroll and found the place
where it is written,
"The Spirit of the Lord is
    upon me,
  because he has chosen me to
  bring good news to the
  poor.
He has sent me to proclaim
    liberty to the captives
  and recovery of sight to the
    blind;

to set free the oppressed
  and announce that the time
    has come
  when the Lord will save his
    people."

Jesus rolled up the scroll, gave
it back to the attendant, and
sat down. All the people in the
synagogue had their eyes fixed
on him, as he said to them,
"This passage of scripture has
come true today, as you heard
it being read."

Luke 4.16-21

What does freedom mean to you?

For me, freedom is

_____

_____

_____

Imagine that you were part of the crowd in the synagogue. What would your reaction have been to what Jesus was saying? Mark the statement which most fits how you would have reacted.

If I'd been in the synagogue I would have:
a) Booed and hissed at Jesus.
b) Believed what he was saying.
c) Not known what to think.
d) Thought Jesus was mad.
e) _____

Paul talked about freedom too:

Freedom is what we have — Christ has set us free! Stand, then, as free people, and do not allow yourselves to become slaves again.

Listen! I, Paul, tell you that if you allow yourselves to be circumcised, it means that Christ is of no use to you at all. Once more I warn any man who allows himself to be circumcised that he is obliged to obey the whole Law. Those of you who try to be put right with God by obeying the Law have cut yourselves off from Christ. You are outside God's grace. As for us, our hope is that God will put us right with him; and this is what we wait for by the power of God's Spirit working through our faith. For when we are in union with Christ Jesus, neither circumcision nor the lack of it makes any difference at all; what matters is faith that works through love.

Galatians 5.1-6

What do you think Paul meant when he talked about freedom through Jesus Christ?

I think Paul meant: (Tick one)
a) That I can do as I like.
b) That we can forget the laws that God gave to Moses.
c) That we no longer have responsibilities.
d) That we can love God and each other without being imprisoned by rules.
e) _____

Paul thought that Christians who let themselves be circumcised were still relying on the law. They didn't realize that Jesus Christ had set them free. They were still prisoners.

Today, we aren't bothered about circumcision. Other everyday worries imprison us. What keeps you behind bars? Write about these things in the box on the next page:

How do you react to the claim that Jesus can make us free from all that keeps us imprisoned? (Tick one)

a) I don't feel free, so it can't be true.
b) I don't know what freedom is.
c) I am beginning to understand the claim more.
d) _____

Next session we are going to consider how we can be free with God's help.

My action point for this week is:

_____
_____
_____

SESSION SEVEN

FREEDOM

Finding out about our new life in Jesus.

This is how I got on with my action point. I found that

_____
_____
_____

Last session we learnt how Jesus sets us free. What did you learn?

I learnt

_____

_____

_____

---

* The Jewish people hoped that God's special agent would be a military leader.
* They wanted him to stop the rule of the Roman people over them.
* The early Christians believed that God's special agent did not come to end human evil, but to conquer the basis of that evil.
* He did this by overthrowing evil spirits and Satan.

Paul said:

You have died with Christ and are set free from the ruling spirits of the universe. Why, then, do you live as though you belonged to this world? Why do you obey such rules as "Don't handle this," "Don't taste that," "Don't touch the other"? All these refer to things which become useless once they are used; they are only man-made rules and teachings. Of course such rules appear to be based on wisdom in their forced worship of angels, and false humility, and severe treatment of the body; but they have no real value in controlling physical passions.

You have been raised to life with Christ, so set your hearts on the things that are in heaven, where Christ sits on his throne at the right-hand side of God. Keep your minds fixed on things there, not on things here on earth. For you have died, and your life is hidden with Christ in God. Your real life is Christ and when he appears, then you too will appear with him and share his glory!

Colossians 2.20—3.4

---

* We are free because we are put right with God through our faith in Jesus Christ.
* This means that we have new life and are no longer bound by the way we used to live.

What else does Paul say we are set free from?

Paul says we are set free from

_____

_____

_____

What do you think this means?

27

I think Paul means that

_____

_____

_____

Paul talks about setting our hearts on things in heaven. What do you think this means?

I think Paul means: (Tick one)
a) I should pray and read my Bible all day.
b) I should think a lot about heaven.
c) I should try and live as Jesus would like me to.
d) _____

Jesus said:

When the people found Jesus on the other side of the lake, they said to him, "Teacher, when did you get here?"

Jesus answered, "I am telling you the truth: you are looking for me because you ate the bread and had all you wanted, not because you understood my miracles. Do not work for food that goes bad; instead, work for the food that lasts for eternal life . This is the food which the Son of Man will give you, because God, the Father, has put his mark of approval on him."

So they asked him, "What can we do in order to do what God wants us to do?"

Jesus answered, "What God wants you to do is to believe in the one he sent."

They replied, "What miracle will you perform so that we may see it and believe you? What will you do? Our ancestors ate manna in the desert, just as the scripture says, 'He gave them bread from heaven to eat.' "

"I am telling you the truth," Jesus said. "What Moses gave you was not the bread from heaven; it is my Father who gives you the real bread from heaven. For the bread that God gives is he who comes down from heaven and gives life to the world."

"Sir," they asked him, "give us this bread always."

"I am the bread of life," Jesus told them. "He who comes to me will never be hungry; he who believes in me will never be thirsty."

John 6.25-35

★ Jesus used the example of men being physically hungry to talk to them about a deeper hunger.
★ This is spiritual hunger.

What do you think Jesus means when he says that anyone who goes to him will never be hungry or thirsty?

I think it means that: (Tick as many as apply)
a) I'll have a constant supply of food.
b) I'll never be lost and alone again, because Jesus will supply all my needs.
c) I can know what God wants me to do.
d) I have a new life in Jesus that can keep me completely satisfied.
e) _____

Sometimes the way we live makes us feel hungry. I feel hungry when: (Tick all that apply)
a) I am jealous.
b) I don't pay my fare.
c) I argue with someone close to me.
d) I don't do the things I should, or do things that I shouldn't.
e) I do things that make me forget about God.
f) _____

If we let Jesus "feed us", we have new life. What does this mean to you? To me, to have new life means: (Tick one)
a) That I will never do bad things again.
b) That Jesus helps me to understand what life is about.
c) That my life has direction and purpose because I love Jesus.
d) That Jesus will help me not to do bad things, but even if I do he will still love me.
e) That Jesus will show me how to live my life properly.
f) _____

If we have faith in Jesus, we have a new life. Jesus satisfies us spiritually and helps us to live as he wants us to. The way we live shows that we have faith in Jesus and are right with God. Next session we'll see how.

My action point for this week is:

_____

_____

_____

SESSION EIGHT

FREEDOM

Thinking about putting others first.

This is how I got on with my action point. I found that

_____

_____

_____

Last session we all learnt something about how Jesus gives us
new life. What did you learn?

I learnt

_____

_____

_____

We can learn about how we should live by reading about Jesus
and what others said about him.

Paul said:

Your life in Christ makes you strong, and his love comforts you. You have fellowship with the Spirit, and you have kindness and compassion for one another. I urge you, then, to make me completely happy by having the same thoughts, sharing the same love, and being one in soul and mind. Don't do anything from selfish ambition or from a cheap desire to boast, but be humble towards one another, always considering others better than yourselves. And look out for one another's interests, not just for your own. The attitude you should have is the one that Christ Jesus had:

He always had the nature of
    God,
    but he did not think that
        by force he should try to
        become equal with God.
Instead of this, of his own free
    will he gave up all he had,
    and took the nature of a
    servant.
He became like man
    and appeared in human
    likeness.

He was humble and walked the
    path of obedience all the
    way to death —
his death on the cross.
For this reason God raised him
    to the highest place above
    and gave him the name that
    is greater than any other
    name.
And so, in honour of the name
    of Jesus

all beings in heaven, on
    earth, and in the world
    below
will fall on their knees,
and all will openly proclaim
    that Jesus Christ is Lord,
to the glory of God the
    Father.

Philippians 2.1-11

What can we learn about how we should live from this
description of Jesus? Write what you have learnt here.

What do you think it means for Jesus to make you strong?

I think it means

When has he done it?

Jesus has made me strong when

Jesus said:

An argument broke out among
the disciples as to which one
of them should be thought of
as the greatest. Jesus said to
them, "The kings of the
pagans have power over their
people, and the rulers are
called 'Friends of the People'.
But this is not the way it is
with you; rather, the greatest
one among you must be like
the youngest, and the leader
must be like the servant. Who
is greater, the one who sits
down to eat or the one who
serves him? The one who sits
down, of course. But I am
among you as one who serves.

31

"You have stayed with me all through my trials; and just as my Father has given me the right to rule, so I will give you the same right. You will eat and drink at my table in my Kingdom, and you will sit on thrones to rule over the twelve tribes of Israel."

Luke 22.24-30

Now think of two ways in which you could show more concern for others.

I could show more concern for others by:

a) _____

b) _____

These passages tell us that we should "look out for one another's interests". Put a mark on this scale to indicate how much you think you do this:

concern for
other people

not bothered about
other people

L_____J

Mohammed Ali loves to tell everyone that he's the greatest. What makes you feel that you deserve lots of praise?

I feel that I deserve praise because I: (Tick as many as appropriate)

a) Don't gossip about others.
b) Do the old lady's shopping.
c) Put a lot in the collection.
d) Go to church twice on Sunday.
e) _____

Do you think it's right to want praise for these things? (Circle the answer that you think applies)

I $\frac{should}{should\ not}$ always want praise for the things I do.

We help others to see Jesus by being humble like Jesus. Next session we'll look at how we can love others too.

My action point for this week is:

_____

_____

_____

SESSION NINE

Thinking about how we can love each other.

This is how I got on with my action point. I found that

_____

_____

_____

Last session we learnt about putting others first. What did you learn?

I learnt

_____

_____

_____

The Bible says that we should love each other. What does this mean to you?

When I say I love someone I mean that

_____

_____

_____

Judas was one of Jesus's disciples. This is what he did:

After Jesus had said this, he was deeply troubled and declared openly, "I am telling you the truth: one of you is going to betray me."

The disciples looked at one another, completely puzzled about whom he meant. One of the disciples, the one whom Jesus loved, was sitting next to Jesus. Simon Peter motioned to him and said, "Ask him whom he is talking about."

So that disciple moved closer to Jesus' side and asked, "Who is it, Lord?"

Jesus answered, "I will dip

some bread in the sauce and give it to him; he is the man." So he took a piece of bread, dipped it, and gave it to Judas, the son of Simon Iscariot. As soon as Judas took the bread, Satan entered him. Jesus said to him, "Be quick about what you are doing!" None of the others at the table understood why Jesus said this to him. Since Judas was in charge of the money bag, some of the disciples thought that Jesus had told him to go and buy what they needed for the festival, or to give something to the poor.

Judas accepted the bread and went out at once. It was night.

After Judas had left, Jesus said, "Now the Son of Man's glory is revealed; now God's glory is revealed through him. And if God's glory is revealed through him, then God will reveal the glory of the Son of Man in himself, and he will do so at once. My children, I shall not be with you very much longer. You will look for me; but I tell you now what I told the Jewish authorities, 'You cannot go where I am going.' And now I give you a new commandment: love one another. As I have loved you, so you must love one another. If you have love for one another, then everyone will know that you are my disciples."

John 13.21-35

How do you think Judas felt when he betrayed Jesus?

When he betrayed Jesus I think Judas must have felt: (Tick one)
a) Really bad.
b) Very sorry, but unable to stop himself.
c) That Jesus deserved what he got.
d) That he had let Jesus down.
e) _____

We all let Jesus down when we do things that he would not like us to. What sort of things do you do? Write about them below:

For some, love is:
Doing the washing up together
or
Remembering her favourite brand of chocolates.

Paul told us:

I may be able to speak the languages of men and even of angels, but if I have no love, my speech is no more than a noisy gong or a clanging bell. I may have the gift of inspired preaching; I may have all knowledge and understand all secrets; I may have all the faith needed to move mountains — but if I have no love, I am nothing. I may give away everything I have, and even give up my body to be burnt — but if I have no love, this does me no good.

Love is patient and kind: it is not jealous or conceited or proud; love is not ill-mannered or selfish or irritable; love does not keep a record of wrongs; love is not happy with evil, but is happy with the truth. Love never gives up; and its faith, hope, and patience never fail.

Love is eternal. There are inspired messages, but they are temporary; there are gifts of speaking in strange tongues, but they will cease; there is knowledge, but it will pass. For our gifts of knowledge and of inspired messages are only partial; but when what is perfect comes, then what is partial will disappear.

When I was a child, my speech, feelings, and thinking were all those of a child; now that I am a man, I have no more use for childish ways. What we see now is like a dim image in a mirror; then we shall see face to face. What I know now is only partial; then it will be complete — as complete as God's knowledge of me.

Meanwhile these three remain: faith, hope, and love; and the greatest of these is love.

I Corinthians 13

For Paul love is ...
(add Paul's descriptions into these speech bubbles)

Draw a picture or write a few sentences about times when you are not loving enough.

God can help you with these things.
Ask him to help right now.

Please God, help me to be more loving by

_____

_____

Thank you.

* We keep God's laws when we love each other.
* Jesus helps us to want to love each other.
* This means that with Jesus's help we are no longer slaves to rules.
* So we are free to live as God wants us to.

Next session see why faith must lead to action.

My action point for this week is:

_____

_____

_____

SESSION TEN

LOVE

Thinking about how we live.

This is how I got on with my action point.

I found that

_____

_____

_____

In the last few sessions, we've been thinking about how Jesus wants us to live and what this means. Jesus had some strong words to say to his followers:

"When the Son of Man comes as King and all the angels with him, he will sit on his royal throne, and the people of all the nations will be gathered before him. Then he will divide them into two groups, just as a shepherd separates the sheep from the goats. He will put the righteous people on his right and the others on his left. Then the King will say to the people on his right, 'Come, you that are blessed by my Father! Come and possess the kingdom which has been prepared for you ever since the creation of the world. I was hungry and you fed me, thirsty and you gave me a drink, I was a stranger and you received me in your homes, naked and you clothed me; I was sick and you took care of me, in prison and you visited me.'

"The righteous will then answer him, 'When, Lord, did we ever see you hungry and feed you, or thirsty and give you a drink? When did we ever see you a stranger and welcome you in our homes, or naked and clothe you? When did we ever see you sick or in prison, and visit you?' The King will reply, 'I tell you, whenever you did this for one of the least important of these brothers of mine, you did it for me!'

"Then he will say to those on his left, 'Away from me, you that are under God's curse! Away to the eternal fire which has been prepared for the Devil and his angels! I was hungry but you would not feed me, thirty but you would not give me a drink; I was a stranger but you would not welcome me in your homes, naked but you would not clothe me; I was sick and in prison but you would not take care of me.'

"Then they will answer him, 'When, Lord, did we ever see you hungry or thirsty or a stranger or naked or sick or in prison, and would not help you?' The King will reply, 'I tell you, whenever you refused to help one of these least important ones, you refused to help me.' These, then, will be sent off to eternal punishment, but the righteous will go to eternal life."

Matthew 25.31-46

What do you think Jesus meant when he said, "The King will reply, 'I tell you, whenever you did this for one of the least important of these brothers of mine, you did it for me' "?

I think Jesus meant

_____

_____

_____

> ★ Jesus didn't just mean that his followers should look after him.
> ★ Jesus says that we must care about other people if we truly want to be like him.

Jesus, one of Jesus's followers wrote:

My brothers, what good is it for someone to say that he has faith if his actions do not prove it? Can that faith save him? Suppose there are brothers or sisters who need clothes and don't have enough to eat. What good is there in your saying to them, "God bless you! Keep warm and eat well!" — if you don't give them the necessities of life? So it is with faith: if it is alone and includes no actions, then it is dead.

But someone will say, "One person has faith, another has actions." My answer is, "Show me how anyone can have faith without actions. I will show you my faith by my actions." Do you believe that there is only one God? Good! The demons also believe — and tremble with fear. You fool! Do you want to be shown that faith without actions is useless? How was our ancestor Abraham put right with God?

It was through his actions, when he offered his son Isaac on the altar. Can't you see? His faith and his actions worked together; his faith was made perfect through his actions. And the scripture came true that said, "Abraham believed God, and because of his faith God accepted him as righteous." And so Abraham was called God's friend. You see, then, that it is by his actions that a person is put right with God, and not by his faith alone.

It was the same with the prostitute Rahab. She was put right with God through her actions, by welcoming the Israelite spies and helping them to escape by a different road.

So then, as the body without the spirit is dead, so also faith without actions is dead.

James 2.14-26

Write about the things that your church could be doing to help others.

My church could be helping others by:

_____

_____

_____

_____

How could you start these things happening?

I could help to start

_____

_____

_____

_____

I could interest other people in doing them too by

_____

_____

_____

_____

In this booklet we have been thinking about:
How we should live now that we are right with God.

What are the most important things that you have learnt?

I have learnt that I must try and show my faith by_____

_____

_____

_____

_____

_____

_____

James also wrote:

**But whoever looks closely into
the perfect law that sets
people free, who keeps on
paying attention to it and does
not simply listen and then
forget it, but puts it into
practice — that person will be
blessed by God in what he
does.** **James 1.25**

Has God's perfect law set you free?

Now use this verse as the basis for a prayer asking God to set you free and to help you to put into practice all you've learnt.

My action point for this week is:

_____
_____
_____

If you have found this booklet helpful, further sessions can be found in "Further Steps in Faith" to be published soon.